Little Things Make Big Differences

A Story about Malaria

Story by Rev. John Nunes & Monique Nunes

Art by Mark Schroder

CONCORDIA PUBLISHING HOUSE · SAINT LOUIS

This book is dedicated
to the **2000 African children**
who die **every day** from malaria.

Published by Concordia Publishing House
3558 S. Jefferson Avenue, St. Louis, MO 63118-3968
1-800-325-3040 • www.cph.org

Text: Copyright © 2010 Lutheran World Relief
Illustrations: Copyright © 2010 Concordia Publishing House. Art on pages 28-29, 31 © iStockphoto.com.

Manufactured in China.

1 2 3 4 5 6 7 8 9 10   19 18 17 16 15 14 13 12 11 10

"Jambo"

That's how you say hello in my language, Swahili. Hi! My name is Rehema, and I live in Tanzania. That's a country in East Africa. It's a wonderful place to live; we have beautiful mountains and beaches and warm weather. Mount Kilimanjaro is in Tanzania. It's the highest mountain in all of Africa! I've never been there, but someday I would like to go.

Lots of people here earn their living by farming. My father and mother are farmers. They grow **bananas** and **tomatoes** and **chili peppers** and **corn**. We also raise **pigs** and **chickens**. I like helping out on the farm by feeding the chickens and picking the tomatoes when they get ripe.

For breakfast, I usually eat porridge and maybe a freshly laid egg or a piece of fruit—banana or mango or pineapple. The fruit here is so fresh and delicious! Then I put on my uniform, a green skirt and a white shirt, and I walk to school with my friends.

I'm only 11, but I already know that when I grow up, I want to be a doctor.

I know it's important to study hard so I can reach my goal. I love going to school and learning new things.

After I come home from school, I do my homework. Then I play with my friends until it's time to eat dinner.

For dinner, my mother usually makes a stew, which we eat with potatoes or rice, and a salad of tomatoes and cucumbers from our garden.

My mother is a great cook! She's starting to teach me the things she knows so one day I can be a great cook too and make traditional Tanzanian dishes like my mother's stew and banana soup and chapati.

Tanzania is home to many magnificent animals. The gentle giraffe, the graceful impala, the enormous elephant, the beautiful zebra, the lazy crocodile, and the majestic lion all live here. But the only animal I'm really scared of is the tiny mosquito!

Have you ever been bitten by a mosquito?

I'll bet you have. In many parts of the world, a mosquito bite is just an annoyance—it itches for a couple of days and makes a bump on your skin, but then it goes away. But where I live, a mosquito bite can be deadly.

I don't remember it, but my parents have told me this story many times. A long time ago, when I was a tiny baby—just a few months old—I almost died because of a mosquito bite. I started having a fever, and my mother took me to the local doctor. He gave her some medicine that was supposed to make my fever go away.

But that night, instead of getting better, I got worse.

I started shaking and trembling and sweating through my nightshirt. My tummy hurt too, but of course I was just a baby and couldn't talk yet, so I just cried and cried.

My father took me to see a neighbor, someone who had just begun to study to be a doctor. The friend took one look at me and told my father, "I think your baby has malaria. You should take her to the hospital immediately."

Now, most people in Tanzania don't have cars, and that includes my family. The only way to get to the hospital was to walk—and it was many miles away. So my father took me home and told my mother what the neighbor had said.

My mother quickly slipped on her sandals, tied me to her back with a piece of cloth, and she and my father set off into the night.

They walked and walked and walked. They walked up hills and down hills. They walked along the dirt path that led out of our village to the main road, and then they walked along the road as it twisted and turned. They didn't talk much during that long journey; they were too worried. They thought I might die before they got me to the hospital.

Once, they stopped to rest their feet, and my mother tried to feed me, but I was too sick to eat. They kept on walking for hours and hours. Finally, about the time the sun came up, they reached the hospital. They were exhausted from the long walk and relieved to finally be somewhere that maybe they could get me some help.

**"I think my baby has malaria,"
my mother told the doctor.**

By this time I was listless, just lying limply on the doctor's table. The doctor took my temperature and asked my parents some questions. They told him about all my symptoms while he examined me.

"Yes, she has malaria," the doctor said. "I will give her some medicine that will make her better. It's a good thing you got here when you did. If she hadn't gotten this medicine, she surely would have died."

For three days, my parents stayed with me in the hospital. The doctor gave me medicine and watched me improve, little by little. Finally, I was well enough to go home.

"Make sure she finishes this medicine," the doctor told my parents as they got ready to begin the long journey home. "Even though she may seem well, the malaria might come back if she doesn't take the rest of the medicine."

The doctor explained to my parents that malaria is a disease that is transmitted by mosquitoes. If a mosquito bites someone who has it and then bites someone else, that person can catch it. He said malaria is a parasite that gets in the blood, and babies and young children are most at risk of getting sick from it.

He told my mother and father that I should sleep under a mosquito net at night to keep the mosquitoes from biting me.

They didn't know that you could get sick from a mosquito bite, and they were surprised to learn how malaria was spread.

Many children in our village had gotten sick with fever, and a few had even died. Sometimes the adults would get sick too, and they would be too weak to work on their farms or go to their jobs. If they couldn't do that, they couldn't earn money for their families.

Now it made sense— the fever was being spread by the mosquitoes that were always buzzing around.

Just like she had done a few days before in the middle of the night, my mother tied me to her back with a piece of cloth, slipped on her sandals, and she and my father set out for their long walk. But this time they were happy. The doctor had saved my life, and now they knew how to keep me from getting malaria again.

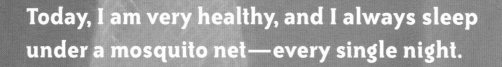

Today, I am very healthy, and I always sleep under a mosquito net—every single night.

So do my parents and my baby brother, Agape. They don't want him to get sick like I did! We get nets that are treated with insecticides, so even if mosquitoes do get in and land on the nets, they can't hurt us.

We learned that there are other things we can do to protect ourselves from getting sick with malaria.

He said that mosquitoes breed in tall grasses and standing water.

We don't have lawn mowers, so my father goes outside and slashes the grass with a big knife when it gets too tall, so the mosquitoes don't breed in it. And we make sure not to have any standing water around the house!

Lately, the pastor at our church has been talking to us about malaria too. It's a big problem here, so he wants to make sure everyone in our church knows about using nets and how to recognize the early symptoms of malaria and that they should go to the doctor before they get too sick.

We go to a Lutheran church, and our pastor told us that Lutherans in the United States, very far away, care about us.

He said they want us to be healthy, so they are working hard to raise money to fight malaria—not just here in Tanzania, but all over the world. The Lutheran churches there are working with Lutheran World Relief to make sure that kids like me have nets to sleep under, that our parents know to take us to the doctor when we get sick, and that the doctors have the right kinds of medicine on hand to treat malaria. They're calling it the Lutheran Malaria Initiative. I think that's pretty exciting!

In church one Sunday, our pastor read to us from Genesis:
"God made the wild animals according to their kinds, the livestock
according to their kinds, and all the creatures that move along the
ground according to their kinds. And God saw that it was good."

**He told us that meant that mosquitoes
are also part of God's creation,
and that just because they can make us sick
doesn't mean they are bad.**

But just like God gave us the wisdom to protect ourselves
from the wild animals of the jungle, He also gave us the wisdom
to protect ourselves from the tiny mosquito.

Kids in the U.S. can do things to help kids like me here in Africa and also in other places where kids catch malaria.

It's part of what God tells us to do in the Bible; it's showing mercy to our neighbors.

Kids in the U.S. and kids in Africa can pray for each other's good health—I'll pray for you to grow up big and strong, and you do the same for me!

Kids in the U.S. can also raise money for the Lutheran Malaria Initiative. I'm lucky that my parents can afford to buy bed nets for my brother and me. But many families here don't have enough money even for food, so they don't get bed nets for their kids, and the kids get sick more often. And then they can't afford to take them to the doctor when they get sick, so they get even sicker. And it all could be avoided if they just had a net to sleep under!

I don't want other kids to get sick like I did, so I'm always telling my friends about malaria.

I want all my friends to grow up healthy and to live out their dreams!

lutheran malaria initiative

UNITED NATIONS FOUNDATION

Restoring health. Inspiring hope.

The **Lutheran Malaria Initiative** is an unprecedented collaborative effort among the Evangelical Lutheran Church in America, The Lutheran Church—Missouri Synod, and Lutheran World Relief to mobilize the nearly eight million Lutherans in the United States to join the battle against malaria—a preventable and treatable disease that kills more than one million people a year.

An expression of our faith and of God's love for all, the Lutheran Malaria Initiative (LMI) will educate U.S. Lutherans about malaria, advocate for global health initiatives, and raise funds to help combat malaria. By combining proven field strategies, experience, expertise, and resources, LMI brings together a worldwide network of Lutheran congregations, partner churches, missionaries, and service providers in the fight against malaria. For generations, Lutherans have been a powerful force for change, and LMI continues that faithful tradition. The three LMI partners are excited about this campaign and look forward to a national launch in the coming months.

The Lutheran Malaria Initiative is made possible through a partnership with the United Nations Foundation.

**Visit www.lutheranmalaria.org
for more information and to get involved!**

What can you do?

Pray

Pray for those who suffer from malaria and for those who are working to prevent, treat, and contain the disease.

Learn

Learn more about malaria and LMI's work. Invite your friends, family, congregation, and community to learn with you.

Advocate

Write a letter to your senator or representative and ask them to support funding for programs to prevent, treat, and contain malaria.

Give

Hold a fund-raiser at your church or school to raise money for LMI.

MALARIA FACTS:

More than **500 million people get sick** with malaria every year.

Each year, 1 million people, most of them children in Africa, die of malaria.

That's **2,880 deaths a day;** **120 deaths an hour;** one death every **30 seconds.**

Poor people are most at risk.

Malaria is preventable and treatable, and you can do something to help!

WHO: http://www.who.int/features/factfiles/malaria/en/index.html   25 April 2007 / CDC

About the Authors

Rev. John Nunes is president and CEO of Lutheran World Relief. His wife, Monique, is a principal of Baltimore Lutheran School. Effusive thanks to Emily Sollie for her careful research and her prayerful literary contribution.

About the Illustrator

Mark Schroder is a nationally recognized illustrator. He grew up in Pittsburgh, Pennsylvania, and has lived in several U.S. states, the Caribbean, and Europe. Mark and his wife, Nicole, live in Denver, Colorado. They are the parents of three daughters: Anya, Caroline, and Megan.

About the Organization

Lutheran World Relief is a ministry of the Evangelical Lutheran Church in America (ELCA), The Lutheran Church—Missouri Synod (LCMS), individuals, and parish groups in international relief, development, advocacy, and social responsibility.

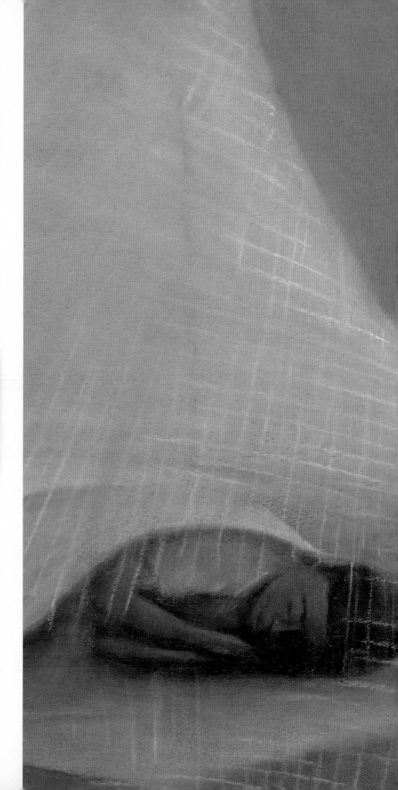

One little bite from **one little mosquito** doesn't seem like a big thing, but if that mosquito carries the parasite that **causes malaria**, its bite can be very serious.

Malaria is one of common infectious diseases, and it can be deadly. Each year, one million people die of malaria—**that's one death every 30 seconds.**

In Africa, 75 percent of the malaria victims are children. Prevention is not only possible, but it's simple. To learn how you can help, visit **lwr.org** or **lutheranmalaria.org**.

Little Things Make Big Differences

is a story about Rehema, a young girl who lives in the African country of Tanzania. When she was a baby, Rehema was infected with malaria, but because her parents were able to get treatment for her, she survived. In these pages, Rehema describes what children in the United States can do to help fight malaria: pray, learn, and advocate for support.

Concordia Publishing House
www.cph.org

ISBN 13: 978-0-7586-1
ISBN 10: 0-7586-1

9 780758 616654

Children/Pictu
56-